L. FRANK BAUM'S

THE WIZARD OF OZ

RETOLD BY **MARTIN POWELL**
ILLUSTRATED BY **JORGE BREAK**
COLOUR BY **BENNY FUENTES**

Raintree

L. FRANK BAUM'S

THE WIZARD OF OZ

Ⓡ **www.raintreepublishers.co.uk**
Visit our website to find out
more information about
Raintree books.

Phone 0845 6044371
Fax +44 (0) 1865 312263
Email myorders@capstonepub.co.uk

Customers from outside the UK please telephone +44 1865 312262

Raintree is an imprint of Capstone Global Library Limited, a company incorporated in
England and Wales having its registered office at 7 Pilgrim Street, London, EC4V 6LB –
Registered company number: 6695582

"Raintree" is a registered trademark of Pearson Education Limited, under licence to
Capstone Global Library Limited

Text © Stone Arch Books 2010
First published in hardback and paperback the United Kingdom by
Capstone Global Library 2010
The moral rights of the proprietor have been asserted.

Art Director: Bob Lentz
Designer: Bob Lentz
Creative Director: Heather Kindseth
Editorial Director: Michael Dahl
Editor: Donald Lemke
Associate Editor: Sean Tulien
UK Editor: Laura Knowles
Originated by Capstone Global Library Ltd
Printed and bound in China by Leo Paper Products Ltd

ISBN 978 1 406214 16 1 (hardback)
14 13 12 11 10
10 9 8 7 6 5 4 3 2 1

ISBN 978 1 406214 20 8 (paperback)
14 13 12 11 10
10 9 8 7 6 5 4 3 2 1

British Library Cataloguing in Publication Data
A full catalogue record for this book is available from the British Library.

CONTENTS

CAST OF CHARACTERS

THE **WICKED WITCH**
OF THE **WEST**

SCARECROW

LION

The great cyclone raised Dorothy's little house higher and higher, carrying it away.

It was dark and windy, but Dorothy remained brave and held little Toto close to her.

Then, as quickly as it began, the howling stopped. A sudden shock made the girl catch her breath.

Their house was safely on the ground again.

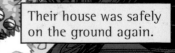

This doesn't look like Kansas, Toto.

MUNCHKIN LAND

There must be some mistake!

I've never killed anything in my whole life!

Not you, perhaps, but your house did.

THE JOURNEY TO THE GREAT OZ

Just stay on the Yellow Brick Road, and all will be well!

Thank you so much, Good Witch. I wish you could come with me.

I cannot do that, but I can give you my magic kiss which will protect you.

Don't be afraid, my child.

Very soon the Wonderful Wizard of Oz will send you home.

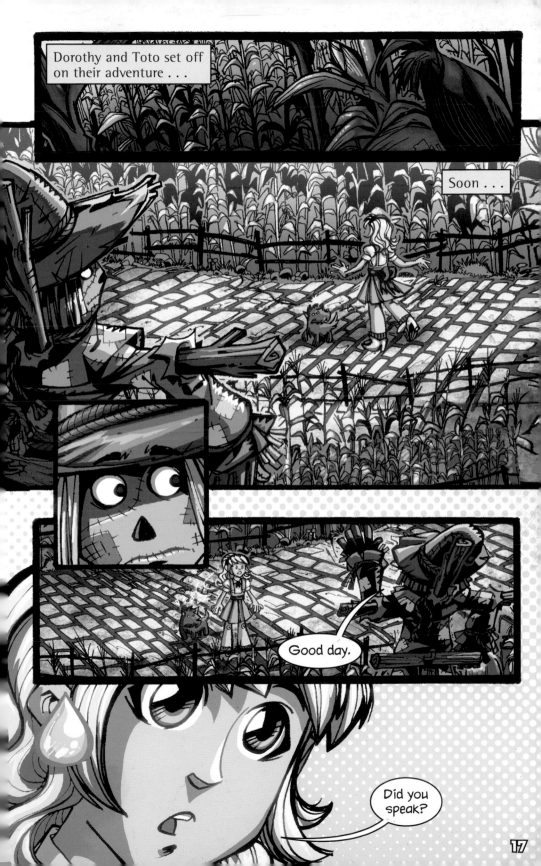

It's a man made of tin! And I think I hear him breathing!

Are you all right, Tin Man?

We're on our way to the Emerald City, to see the Wizard of Oz.

That sounds exciting! Why do you wish to see the Wizard?

Brains, huh? They aren't the best things in the world, you know.

What do you mean? What's better than brains?

I want the Wizard to send me and Toto back home to Kansas.

And the Scarecrow wants some brains put in his head.

I would ask the Wizard for a heart. Do you think he might give me one?

How do you know you'll like having a heart when you get one?

I don't see why not. Come with us, and we'll ask him.

I had a heart once. I was in love with a Munchkin girl, but the Wicked Witch of the West hates to see anyone happy.

She enchanted my axe with an evil spell, and it chopped me into pieces.

"A clever tinsmith managed to save me. He made me this body of tin . . . but he forgot to give me a heart."

If Oz grants my wish, I'll return to these woods and ask my little Munchkin girl to marry me.

It will happen, Tin Man! I know it will!

Dorothy and her new friends kept travelling after the sun had set . . .

How long until we are out of the forest?

Don't worry. As long as I have my axe, I'll protect us all!

GRRRRRRrr

Something's behind the trees!

Besides, the Good Witch protected you with her kiss.

Did you hear that?!

Nothing can harm you.

There it is again!

I hear it too!

GGRrrrrrrr

26

CHAPTER 4

THE WONDERFUL CITY OF OZ

I AM OZ, THE GREAT AND TERRIBLE!
Who are you, and why do you seek me?!
I am Dorothy, the Small and Meek. We've come to ask you for help.

CHAPTER 5

SEARCH FOR THE WICKED WITCH

At the castle of the Wicked Witch of the West . . .

The soldier said all we need to do is think of the Wicked Witch, and she'll find us.

That will be easy. I can't stop worrying about her!

THERE YOU ARE, MY PRETTY LITTLE THINGS!

Oh, no! A storm is coming!

Run! The Wicked Witch has found us!

It's worse than that! Look!

Soon . . .

WELCOME, DOROTHY OF KANSAS.

I'M SURE YOU KNOW WHO I AM, AND THE TERRIBLE THINGS I CAN DO.

NOW GIVE ME THOSE SILVER SLIPPERS, OR ELSE!

No! You can't have them!

And I wear the mark of the Good Witch, so you can't hurt me!

BARK BARK!

Dorothy was right. The Wicked Witch could not hurt her.

Instead, the evil woman used her magic . . .

47

48

Just as her sister had commanded the Munchkins, the Wicked Witch of the West had ruled the Winkies.

The Wicked Witch's spell has been broken!

You are no longer her slaves!

We're free!

The Winkies sewed Scarecrow back together again and gave him a walking stick.

Thank you, my friends. I will no longer stumble as I travel.

Look at what I found in the Wicked Witch's cupboard.

I shall give this helmet to the Wizard to prove that the Witch is truly gone.

CHAPTER 6

DISCOVERY OF OZ

Later, in the Emerald City . . .

Back so soon? How did you escape the Wicked Witch?

I melted her with water!

That is good news, indeed!

Come back tomorrow, and I might grant your wishes.

Toto, come back! What are you doing?

Tomorrow? But you've had plenty of time already!

SILENCE! The Great and Terrible Oz has spoken!

54

As for you, your Majesty, one sip of this and courage will always be inside you!

COURAGE

Oh, joy! I promise to rule with kindness and bravery!

Thank you for helping them, Oz. They are good friends and deserve good things.

Get a good night's sleep tonight, Dorothy. Because tomorrow . . .

. . . we're both going home!

I am going to visit my wizard brother who lives far away in the clouds!

He is very wise!

While I am gone, Scarecrow will rule in my place!

Toto! This is no time to play! The Wizard is taking us back home!

MEEOW!

BARK BARK!

56

Did it work, Toto?

Goodness gracious!

The colour had returned to Aunt Em's cheeks. And Uncle Henry, who had never smiled, now laughed until he cried.

My darling child! Where in the world did you come from?

From the Land of Oz! And Toto was there, too!

Oh, Aunt Em! I'm so glad to be home!

TALES OF OZ

Considered by many to be the first American fairy tale, the original version of *The Wonderful Wizard of Oz* was published in the year 1900. It was a big hit, and its entire first printing sold out. The book has since been translated into more than 40 different languages and published across the world. A signed first-edition copy of the book once sold for almost £100,000!

There are 40 official sequels and prequels to *The Wonderful Wizard of Oz*, including 14 that were written by L. Frank Baum, and 19 written by Ruth Plumly Thompson. But the original book, *The Wonderful Wizard of Oz*, is by far the most popular of all the *Oz* books.

The first musical version of *The Wonderful Wizard of Oz* was produced by Baum and Denslow in 1902. It used the same characters and had a long, successful run of nearly 300 shows from 21 January 1903, to 31 December 1904.

Silent film versions of *The Wonderful Wizard of Oz* were made in 1910 and 1925. A seven-minute long animated cartoon was made in 1933.

The first major film version of *Oz* was made by MGM and released in 1939, entitled *The Wizard of Oz*. It featured many musical numbers, including "Somewhere Over the Rainbow," which was chosen as the greatest movie song of all time by the American Film Institute in 2004. The movie also won several Academy Awards, including Best Picture, in the year of its release.

The Wizard of Oz movie made only a small profit upon its original release. However, the film was re-released in 1948 after the end of World War II to much greater success. Even so, the film didn't begin to make a profit for MGM until after 1976!

The Wiz was a 1978 movie starring Diana Ross as Dorothy and Michael Jackson as the Scarecrow. It exclusively featured African-American actors.

The Wizard of Oz was made into a video game for the Super Nintendo gaming system in 1993. It was based on the 1939 film.

The Wizard of Oz on Ice was a touring production that performed across the world from 1995 to 1999.

Wicked is a 2003 musical based on the book *Wicked: The Life and Times of the Wicked Witch of the West* by Gregory Maguire. It tells the story of how the Wicked Witch of the West came to be so cruel. *Wicked* broke box office records in New York, Los Angeles, Chicago, and St. Louis in the United States, and London in the United Kingdom.

ABOUT THE AUTHOR

LYMAN FRANK BAUM was an American author, poet, playwright, actor, and filmmaker. In 1900, Baum published *The Wonderful Wizard of Oz*. It is considered to be a classic of children's literature to this day. He also wrote 13 sequels to *Oz*, as well as a total of 55 novels, 82 short stories, and more than 200 poems. He is considered by many to be a visionary, and had predicted that colour TV and mobile phones would be quite common in the near future.

ABOUT THE RETELLING AUTHOR

MARTIN POWELL has been a freelance writer since 1986. He has written hundreds of stories, many of which have been published by Disney, Marvel, Tekno Comix, Moonstone Books, and others. In 1989, Powell received an Eisner Award nomination for his graphic novel *Scarlet in Gaslight*. This award is one of the highest comic book honours.

ABOUT THE ILLUSTRATOR

JORGE BREAK was born in Mexico City, Mexico. At an early age, he developed a love of reading comic books and drawing. Jorge began working as a graphic designer and illustrator in 1993 and was published for the first time in *MAD Magazine* (Mexican Edition). Jorge has also illustrated for the Mexican Edition of Captain Tsubasa (a popular football Japanese-style manga cartoon), and from 2000 to 2007 he has worked on his own series, Meteorix 5.9.

GLOSSARY

balloonist person who pilots and maintains hot air balloons

bleak empty and depressing, or without hope

cyclone big storm with very strong, swirling winds

enchanted something that has been enchanted has been put under a magic spell or seems magical

ferocious very fierce and savage

majesty formal title for a king or queen

meek quiet, humble, and obedient

naive not very experienced, or too trusting

poppies type of garden plant with large, red flowers

protect guard or keep something safe from harm

sensitive easily hurt or saddened

spell word or words supposed to have magical powers

wicked very bad, cruel, or evil

wizard person believed to have magic powers

DISCUSSION QUESTIONS

1. If you had a chance to ask the Wizard of Oz for one gift, what would it be? Would you ask for courage, like the lion, or something else? Explain your answer.

2. Why do you think Dorothy wanted to return home so badly? Would you have wanted to stay in the Land of Oz? Why or why not?

3. Have you seen or read other versions of *The Wizard of Oz*? If so, in what ways were those versions different to this story? In what ways were they the same?

WRITING PROMPTS

1. What do you think happened to the other characters when Dorothy left the Emerald City? Choose a character and write about how they lived after Dorothy was gone.

2. The journey to the Emerald City was dangerous but also exciting. Write about the most exciting trip you've ever taken. Where did you go? What made the experience so memorable?

3. Dorothy's Silver Slippers had the power to take her home. If you had the power to be transported anywhere in the world, where would you go? Write about your choice and what you would do when you got there.

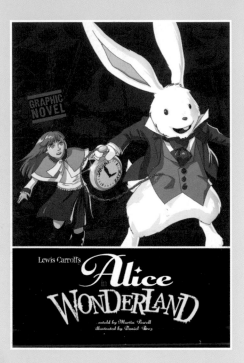

ALICE IN WONDERLAND

One day, a young girl named Alice spots a frantic White Rabbit wearing a waistcoat and carrying a pocket watch. She follows the hurrying creature down a hole into the magical world of Wonderland. While there, Alice meets more crazy creatures, and plays a twisted game of croquet with the Queen of Hearts. But when the Queen turns against her, this dream-like world quickly becomes a nightmare.

THE JUNGLE BOOK

In the jungles of India, a pack of wolves discover a young boy. They name the boy Mowgli and protect him against dangers, including Shere Khan, the most savage tiger in the jungle. As Mowgli grows up, he learns the ways of the jungle from Bagheera the panther, Baloo the wise bear, and other animals. Soon, he must decide whether to remain among beasts or embrace his own kind.

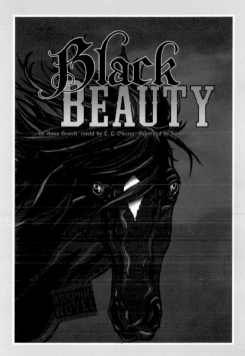

20,000 LEAGUES UNDER THE SEA

Scientist Pierre Aronnax and his trusty servant set sail to hunt a sea monster. With help from Ned Land, the world's greatest harpooner, the men soon discover that the creature is really a high-tech submarine. To keep this secret from being revealed, the sub's leader, Captain Nemo, takes the men hostage. Now, each man must decide whether to trust Nemo or try to escape this underwater world.

BLACK BEAUTY

A handsome colt named Black Beauty has a happy childhood growing up in the peaceful countryside. In his later years, he encounters terrible illness and a frightening stable fire. Things go from bad to worse when Black Beauty's new owners begin renting him out for profit. Black Beauty endures a life of mistreatment and disrespect in a world that shows little regard for the wellbeing of animals.

GRAPHIC REVOLVE

If you have enjoyed this story, there are many more exciting
tales for you to discover in the Graphic Revolve collection...

20,000 Leagues Under the Sea

Alice in Wonderland

Black Beauty

Dracula

Frankenstein

Gulliver's Travels

The Hound of the Baskervilles

The Hunchback of Notre Dame

The Jungle Book

King Arthur and the Knights of the Round Table

Robin Hood

The Strange Case of Dr Jekyll and Mr Hyde

Treasure Island

The War of the Worlds